LEAST I COULD DO
THE BLACK AND WHITE COLLECTION

 S0-BEZ-386

NOIR ET BLANC

BY RYAN SOHMER & LAR DESOUZA

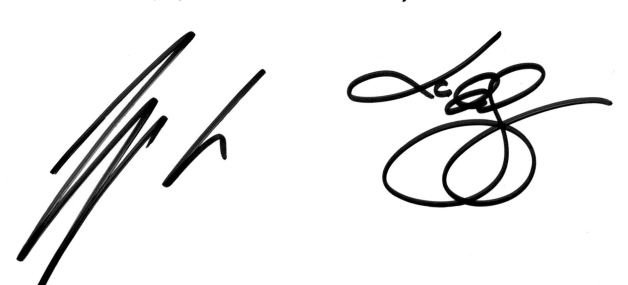

Blind Ferret Entertainment © 2010

Least I Could Do is distributed by Blind Ferret Entertainment.

Noir et Blanc Copyright ©2010 by Blind Ferret Entertainment, Inc.
All rights reserved. Printed in China.

No part of this book may be reproduced or transmitted in any form or by any means, electronic
or mechanical, including photocopying, recording, or by any information storage or retrieval system,
without permission in writing from the Publisher, except in the case of reprints in the context
of reviews. For information, contact Blind Ferret Entertainment, 8362 Labarre, Montreal, Quebec,
Canada H4P 2E7 .

First paperback edition published 2010.
Second paperback edition published 2010.

www.leasticoulddo.com

ISBN 978-1-926838-01-4

Book Credits

Written by Ryan Sohmer
Strips by Lar deSouza
Book Layout and Cover by Lar deSouza
Edited by Randy Waxman & Susan Sohmer

For Blind Ferret Entertainment

Randy Waxman - President & CEO
Ryan Sohmer - Vice President, Creative Director
Marc Aflalo - Media Director & Public Relations Manager
Lar DeSouza - Art Director
Nick D iFeo - Sales Manager
Stuart Becker - Operations Manager
Ryan McCahan - IT Manager

**When I was four years old,
my parents got me a cabbage patch doll named Elton.**

I still have him. He's very dirty..

The book you're currently holding in your hands is something of a dirty little secret, to my mind at least.

Think of it as you would your teenage years, on the cusp of adulthood. You're awkward, your voice is funny and there is hair in places you're not sure belongs. But still, you soldier on, you learn to manage the aforementioned hair and you adapt, slowly figuring out what it means to be responsible for your actions.

At the inception of Least I Could Do, many years ago (but alas, not in a galaxy far, far away) I hadn't the faintest notion of what I was getting into. Not only that, but as this was my first serialized comic strip, I didn't really know how to write just yet.

And that is what Least I Could Do: Noir & Blanc is.

The beginning, that awkward time where I was discovering the voices of these characters, who they were, the directions their lives would take and incidentally, the one my life took as well.

In an idealized world, we would have presented these first 125 strips to you as they were drawn, by Mr. Trevor Adams. Unfortunately, as little as I knew about writing back then, I knew even less about image quality. That said, the resolution used to created these strips wouldn't have functioned in a print book. Luckily however, we had a solution.

Lar volunteered to redraw the first strips done by Trevor for this print collection, solely in Black & White in order to retain some of the simplicity we had begun with. Never one to pass up the opportunity to write an introduction for a book, I quickly accepted his offer (before his aging mind forgot what he had offered).

Revisiting your past isn't always a pleasant experience, but in this case, ego aside, each and every single strip brought up a wonderful memory.

With that, I leave you to explore the origins of Least I Could Do and the introduction of a man named Rayne.

- Because I Can

"I have every expectation
That my final prayers will go unheard
And my veiled death bed confession
Will not move the Mighty Lord
I'm sure that I'll be sorry
When he slams St. Peter's Gate
But I'll dive right into damnation
With a smile across my face"

For Those
Very First Readers,,

Least I Could Do was,
and always will be,
a learning experience for us.

Thank you for
sticking it out. t

For Tim Hortons

Without your convenient
24 hour drive thrus and
delicious coffee, this book
might never have been.

Would you look at that? The first LICD strip I'd ever written.

BYE BABY.

I LOVE YOU.

I LOVE YOU MORE.

AND CARRIE MAKES FIFTY!

HAPPY ANNIVERSARY!

If my goal was to set the precedent for the thousands of strips to follow, I'd say I succeeded. Obviously, this comic was going to be a classy one. Like Andy Capp classy.

To be precise, it was the second ever published.

More on that cryptic comment at the end of the book!

Looking back, as is the purpose of this book, mind you, one gets the idea that Rayne began his cartoon life as quite the ass. It took quite a bit of time for me to realize that this main character can't be completely unlikeable if I'm going to tell the stories I was planning on telling.

Slowly but surely, Rayne softened up somewhat, and showed us a different side.

SO WHAT HAPPENED TO CARRIE ANYWAY?

IT HAS NOTHING TO DO WITH YOU,

IT'S ME...

...I DON'T LIKE YOU.

HEH.

GOOD TIMES.

My comic timing, or lack thereof, amuses me greatly.

While reading the first few dozens strips, notice that I use the same beat over and over again:

Panel 1: Setup
Panel 2: Setup
Panel 3: Plot Movement or Awkward Pause
Panel 4: Punch line

Crude as this may be, the gravy line gets me everytime. Then I'm left to wonder. Would dating such a girl be that bad?

Once again, my use of subtlety is amazing. The only way to make this a louder more obnoxious strip would be to drive a truck through your living room window.

Lucky for you, I don't know where you live. Yet.

SHARE THE GOOD

TIP 53477 FOR PICKING UP: THE RETARDED FRIEND GAMBIT

THIS IS MY FRIEND MICK,

HE'S MENTALLY CHALLENGED, BUT I TAKE HIM WHEREVER I GO.

I LOVE HIM LIKE A BROTHER.

MAAAAAAAH

OH MY GOD! THAT IS SO SWEET AND SELFLESS.

COME HOME WITH ME?

MAAAAAAAH

GIMME A HEINEKEN.

YOU SURE YOU'RE ALLOWED TO DRINK BEER?

MAAAAAAAH

CHICK HUMOUR

ASK ME!

DO I HAVE TO?

HERE GOES.

HOW WOULD YOU DEFINE A DEER?

IT'S SKINNIER THAN A HORSE!

THIS LESS THAN INTELLIGENT MOMENT BROUGHT TO YOU BY THE CENTRE FOR CONTINUING EDUCATION.

HA HA HA HA HA

WHERE SHE JUST HAPPENS TO ATTEND.

HA HA HA HA HA HA HA

This is the first strip that was taken word for word from a conversation with my very own Issa. I'm still not sure if the general public found it as funny as we did, but what are you going to do?

YOU WANT A WHAT?

YOU HEARD ME.

A GIRLFRIEND.

FINE, BUT LET ME ASK YOU SOMETHING.

GO AHEAD.

DO YOU WANT A GIRLFRIEND BECAUSE YOU'RE READY FOR A SERIOUS COMMITMENT?

WHAT'S OPTION TWO?

BECAUSE YOU'VE BEEN STRIKING OUT A LOT LATELY?

OOOOH, THAT ONE!

One of the very many fun things about starting a brand new project like Least I Could Do, is that you're faced with so many decisions, millions of little forks in the road, that you never know where you're going to end up. Who knows where this would have led if I had decided that Rayne was done playing the field?

(By 'playing the field' I mean being a man-whore. I hope you caught that.)

Back in the day, when I was but a wee lad and spent my weekend evenings in clubs and other such establishments, nothing would provide me with more enjoyment than watching someone strike out on the dance floor.

AND, GO!

SIX SECONDS FOR COMPLETE REJECTION.

NICE.

SOMEONE BUY THIS MAN A HOOKER!

ZOOOM

BAM

YES!

ANOTHER POINT FOR JESUS!

THAT'S RIGHT,

JESUS CHRIST HIMSELF TAKES THE LEAD!

WHAT?

Marc (Mick) and I used to play tennis a few nights a week. It was great fun and a solid workout. Still, the most pleasure we got out of it was inventing new methods of cursing various deities when one of us missed a point.

And no, there were no nuns at the club...though I bet they'd sweat right through those robes.

Eight years later and the answer to that question is still a resounding "NO".

THIS IS HARD FOR ME TO SAY, BUT I THINK I HAVE TO TELL YOU.

YOU CAN TELL ME ANYTHING.

THE DOCTOR SAID I MIGHT HAVE SOMETHING CALLED "HERPES"?

EVER HEARD OF IT?

I'M SURE A LITTLE PENICILLIN WILL CLEAR THAT RIGHT UP!

STD JOKES.

DO THEY EVER GET OLD?

THIS IS A SERIOUS ISSUE.

WHAT IF IT'S A PERMANENT THING?

IT'S NOT FUNNY. STOP LAUGHING.

JUST SAY IT AGAIN.

ERECTILE DIFFICULTY.

As a writer, I quickly learned that a main character can't always win. He can win most of the time, sure, but if you don't throw in a setback from time to time, things will get stale.

And flaccid.

Long time Least I Could Do readers may be scratching their head and trying to figure out exactly who that character is standing next to Mick and John. The astute among you will realize that this is Rob.

SO HOW DID THE GIRL TAKE IT?

THE GIRL?

YEAH, THE GIRL YOU FAILED TO PLEASURE.

AH, THAT GIRL.

AS USUAL, I HANDLED IT WITH RESPECT FOR HER FEELINGS.

IS IT BECAUSE YOU'RE NOT ATTRACTED TO ME?

YEP.

Enjoy his prominence now, as soon he will fade away into the oblivion that contains all forgotten and neglected comic strip characters.

It may seem here that Rayne approves of cheating, but let me assure you, that is far from the reality. He is fond of blackmail though.

Thus concludes the first complete (more than two consecutive strips) story arc I had ever put together. I'm sure I intended for there to be a moral here somewhere but I haven't the faintest idea what that could be.

Use a condom?

PROLONGED PAINFUL ERECTION FTW

©2009 Blind Ferret Entertainment

 Watching Dorothy and the gang traipse their way down the yellow brick road used to be something I did on a yearly basis. The character in that film I've always empathized with however was never the little girl from Kansas or her faithful dog (they'd be fine, I was certain). It was the Wizard. The man with the big mouth who was unable to follow through. Poor guy.

IF HE ONLY HAD A BRAIN

THE GIRL BY THE BAR THINKS YOU'RE CUTE—

NOOOOO!!!

CAN'T BLAME HER...

YOU NEVER, EVER COMPLIMENT HIM.

EVER.

I'VE GOT A NOAH WYLE THING GOING ON.

HE TENDS TO GO ON THESE

EGO BENDERS

AND I HAVE BEEN WORKING OUT...

I AM THE POWERFUL OZ!

EVERY SINGLE TIME.

On an unrelated note, I've been giving serious thought to joining the lollipop guild. I feel I could be an asset.

LET'S SEE DR. PHIL DO THIS

WAS IT SMART TO LEAVE HIM THERE ALONE?

IT WAS EITHER THAT, OR SPEND THE REST OF THE NIGHT LISTENING TO HOW WONDERFUL HE IS.

IN ANY EVENT,

YOU LEFT HIM WITH CAB MONEY, SO WHAT TROUBLE COULD HE GET INTO?

YOU OK?

MY FRIENDS ABANDONED ME HERE WITHOUT A WAY HOME.

MY FEELINGS ARE TRULY HURT.

YOU POOR SWEETIE!

CAN I OFFER YOU A LIFT?

YES, YES YOU MAY.

Where I discover the elusive "PLOT TWIST".

LAST NIGHT WAS GREAT.

YES, YES IT REALLY WAS.

IT'S WEIRD, BUT I ACTUALLY FEEL SOMETHING TOWARDS YOU.

THAT'S NEVER HAPPENED TO ME BEFORE.

REALLY?

BECAUSE THERE'S SOMEONE I WANT YOU TO MEET.

I THINK I COULD HANDLE MEETING YOUR MOM.

NOT MY MOTHER, SILLY...

MY SON.

GOD HATES ME.

The fact that Rayne was even considering a relationship with this girl is an anomaly in itself. This may have been one of the many contributing elements to Rayne's history that caused his disinterest in having one of those....what do you call them? Girlfriends?

RAYNE, THIS IS JORDAN.

ALRIGHT, THIS ISN'T SO BAD. I CAN DO THIS.

GINA IS HOT, SWEET AND I THINK I GENUINELY CARE ABOUT HER...

I'M NOT GOING TO FREAK OUT JUST BECAUSE SHE HAS A KID.

DADDY?

They had cell phones and laptops back in 2003? Who knew?

TODDLING ALONG

 As a newly minted father myself, I find this joke even funnier than I had originally. I'm not sure what that says about my parenting skills, but probably nothing good.

BABY'S FIRST HANGOVER

As an olde timey type dad, I'm looking forward to listening to Sohmer's child rearing with a calloused attitude and unsympathetic ear. Not my fault he didn't heed my warnings.

With the knowledge I possess now, it's come to my attention how factually incorrect this comic is. Breast milk is never kept in the fridge longer than five days.

See?

I be genius.

If you've got breast milk left in the fridge that's more than five days old, then I think you're forgetting to feed the baby.

SINCE WE'VE BEEN TOGETHER RAYNE,

JORDAN AND I COULDN'T BE HAPPIER.

IT'S AS IF YOU FILL A HOLE IN BOTH OUR LIVES THAT WE DIDN'T KNOW WAS THERE.

WHAT I'M TRYING TO SAY RAYNE, IS THAT... WELL...

I LOVE YOU.

YOU'RE THINKING ABOUT BOLTING, AREN'T YOU?

WHY WOULD YOU THINK THAT?

Every man has his relationship breaking point. This is Rayne's.

Babies and dogs, my friends. You want to reel in the females, the secret is babies and dogs.

Extra points for baby dogs.

HOW COME YOU HAVE THE BABY?

GINA LET ME HAVE HIM ONE LAST TIME.

WHY?

WATCH AND LEARN.

...SO AFTER MY WIFE DIED IN THAT HORRIBLE FARMING ACCIDENT, IT WAS JUST ME AND LITTLE ANAKIN.

WE'VE BEEN LONELY,

BUT IT'S HARD TO DATE WHEN YOU HAVE TO BE RESPONSIBLE, CARING AND NURTURING ALL THE TIME.

WHO WOULD WANT TO BE WITH A MAN LIKE THAT?

But not for dog babies.

That's the same damn thing!

Panel 1:
WHAT ARE YOU WATCHING?
WHY?
BUFFY THE VAMPIRE SLAYER.

Panel 2:
YOU KNOW, I'M SO SICK OF PEOPLE RAGGING ON BUFFY.
YES, THE NAME IS A LITTLE OFF PUTTING BUT IT'S A GREAT SHOW.

Panel 3:
THE WRITING IS INTELLIGENT,
THE ACTION SEQUENCES ARE FUN
AND SARAH MICHELLE GELLAR IS INCREDIBLY ENGAGING.
IT'S WONDERFUL ENTERTAINMENT.

Panel 4:
DUDE, WHERE ARE YOUR PANTS?
A BETTER QUESTION WOULD BE "WHERE ARE MY BOXERS?"

I was late to the Buffy: The Vampire Slayer party, but I partied extra hard when I got there. Buffy's recent re-emergence in comics was a pleasing turn of events for me.

Panel 5:
WHAT'S WRONG?
THIS GUY JUST STOLE THE GIRL I WAS INTERESTED IN.
RIGHT BACK.

Panel 6:
HEY BRO, I HEARD YOU COULD HELP ME OUT.
SHOOT.
WERE YOU NERVOUS THE FIRST TIME YOU SLEPT WITH YOUR SISTER,
OR DID IT FEEL NATURAL?

Panel 7:
(no dialogue)

Panel 8:
THAT WAS A NICE THING YOU DID.
IF ONLY WE COULD FIND SOMETHING LARGE AND FIRM TO PRESS AGAINST MY WOUNDS.

Helps out his friends.

At least one redeeming quality in a main character? Check.

Another first, this is a glimpse into what Rayne does for a living. Though he's had career changes since, I miss the days when he was working for the newspaper.

I CAN'T BELIEVE YOU REWROTE ALL MY STUDENTS' REPORT CARDS.

THERE WAS EFFORT THERE, BUT IT WAS WORTH IT.

TELL ME THE PART AGAIN WHEN THE MOTHER STARTED TO JAB YOU WITH YOUR OWN RULER.

I'LL GET YOU BACK FOR THIS.

I PROMISE.

Globe and State
WHY FAT WOMEN SHOULD LEARN HOW TO PURGE AFTER EVERY MEAL

By Rayne Summers

HE DOESN'T MAKE IT EASY

DON'T LOOK AT ME.

THAT'S ACTUALLY WHAT HE WROTE.

For those of you unfamiliar with the term, a 'newspaper' can be described as the Internet, version 0.01.

PROLONGED, PAINFUL AND FANTASTIC

YOU'RE STILL TAKING THE VIAGRA, AREN'T YOU?

I'M WEARING SIX PAIRS OF BOXERS AND I'M STILL SCARED TO STAND UP.

They say you're supposed to call a doctor if your erection lasts for more than four hours.

I disagree with that course of action.

When commercials tell you to 'ask your doctor' if a medicine is right for you, can they ethically refuse any man if this is a side effect?

I don't use sports metaphors often (mostly because I don't know what they mean) but in this case, it was rather fitting.

I know I was surprised at how big a fan of curling you are. Always screaming "Hard! Hard!" I just assumed you were bragging.

Having Rayne more or less on the path to becoming a three dimensional ass of a character, it was time to work on the others. Who was John, and how did he differ from Rayne?

JEBAS! THAT WOMAN IS BEING ATTACKED BY THAT RED MIDGET! COME ON GUYS!

RAYNE, WAIT—

DON'T WORRY MA'AM, I'M COMING!

FLYING NINJA KICK!

SO WE'RE AGREED?

YEP, HE'S NOT ALLOWED NEAR TEQUILA AGAIN.

I'm not proud of this, or confident that sharing this is one of my better ideas, but yes, this strip is based off real events.

A life lesson! Use condoms and don't do hardcore drugs.

My chances of becoming the next pope are increasing.

FLYING NINJA KICK!

PHARMACY

THAT'LL BE $317.54, PLEASE.

MONTHLY CONDOM RUN?

I SHOULD START SNORTING COKE,

IT'S CHEAPER.

My chances of becoming the next pope are decreasing.

This arc was one of my biggest personal motivations for tackling this project. I consider this storyline a real milestone in Sohmer's writing. He surprised the readers and took the characters in a terrific and unexpected direction.

To plays devil's advocate here, it is getting harder and harder to tell a girl's age. I blame Britney Spears for turning an entire generation of girls into slutty dressers.

Yeah. I said it.

SWEET LITTLE SIXTEEN

Trevor's work has great charm but his character designs limited the kind of emotional expression being called for sometimes. I revel in pushing the range of the cast.

I'M NOT GOING TO LIE TO YOU, RAYNE.

SLEEPING WITH A MINOR IS A SERIOUS OFFENSE.

DUE TO MARY'S MOM'S CHARGES AGAINST YOU,

YOU'RE GOING TO HAVE TO REMAIN IN PRISON UNTIL THE TRIAL BEGINS.

ON THE BRIGHT SIDE, WE SHOULD BE ABLE TO STRIKE A DEAL –

BUT WHAT ABOUT MY IDEA?

FOR THE LAST TIME,

"SHE'S A MAN-HUNGRY NYMPH" IS *NOT* A SOLID DEFENSE.

Oh Jebas. I'm starting to remember now where this arc is going.

And there it is.

YOU GUYS REMEMBER WHEN I USED TO SAY THAT IF I EVER GOT SENT TO PRISON I'D FIND THE BIGGEST, MEANEST INMATE I COULD

AND SUBMIT MYSELF TO HIM FOR PROTECTION?

MEET WAYNE.

Anybody who tells you they wouldn't do the exact same thing in this sutation is a liar. Or some kind of super Ninja.

LAVA 25 TO LIFE

HARD TO GET I LIKE THAT.

"I find I'm so excited, I can barely sit still or hold a thought in my head. I think it's the excitement only a free man can feel, a free man at the start of a long journey whose conclusion is uncertain. I hope I can make it across the border. I hope to see my friend and shake his hand. I hope the Pacific is as blue as it has been in my dreams. I hope."
-from Shawshank Redemption (1994)

If you can't make a joke about getting anally raped...I'm not going to finish this sentence.

YOU TRIED TO WHAT?!

ESCAPE FROM PRISON.

OK, FORGET ABOUT THAT.

ALL I WANT YOU TO DO IS CONCENTRATE ON TOMORROW'S TRIAL AND –

CRASH

HA HA HA HA HA HA HA HA HA HA HA HA HA HA HA HA HA HA

WHAT'S SO FUNNY ABOUT FALLING OFF A CHAIR?

JUST THINKING THAT THIS HAS NOT BEEN A GOOD WEEK FOR MY ASS.

From the prisoners, to the lawyer, judge and bailiff - just so many opportunities to craft some awesome moments in comic storytelling.

AH, MR. SUMMERS,

SO GOOD TO SEE YOU AGAIN.

YOU KNOW THE JUDGE? THIS COULD REALLY WORK IN OUR FAVOR.

AFTER YOU BROKE HER HEART, MY DAUGHTER HAD A FEW CONFIDENCE ISSUES.

HOW'S CARRIE DOING, SIR?

SHE'S BEEN HOSPITALIZED FOR ANOREXIA TREATMENT FOR THE LAST FEW MONTHS. BECAUSE OF THINGS YOU SAID TO HER.

HEY, IF YOU HADN'T FED HER FUDGE IN THE FIRST PLACE–

FOR THE LOVE OF GOD, PLEASE SHUT UP.

AFTER CAREFUL CONSIDERATION OF ALL THE FACTS, THE COURT HAS REACHED A VERDICT.

THE SIMPLE CONCLUSION IS THAT MR. SUMMERS WAS NOT AWARE OF MARY'S AGE.

YOUR DAUGHTER, MADAM, SHOULD NOT BE HANGING OUT IN BARS.

Legally speaking, I doubt this argument would hold up in court yet the logic is sound.

Feel free to write your local member of government to see this written into law.

Change begins with you.

DESPITE MY ENORMOUS DISLIKE YOU FOR YOU, MR. SUMMERS,

YOU ARE FREE TO GO.

SO YOU'RE SAYING AS LONG AS I MEET SIXTEEN YEAR OLDS IN BARS, I CAN TAKE THEM HOME LEGALLY?

GET HIM OUT OF HERE NOW.

Despite assuming that he sprang from the forehead of some god, Rayne actually has parents. Insert the saying here about the apple and the tree.

Why do we live in a world where one is forced to wait more than 47 seconds to cook a burrito? Forget curing diseases and inventing flying cars, this is where science should be at.

Now this, this is something I'm insanely proud of. The introduction of Bra-man had the potential to shake the world of super heroes forever.

Sadly, it did not live up to this potential.

YOU HAVE THE MATURITY OF A THREE YEAR OLD.

CALL ME WHEN YOU GROW UP.

WITH BIG BREASTS COME BIG RESPONSIBILITY.

SHE WASN'T IMPRESSED WITH *BRA-MAN?*

Another moment that I felt the need to artistically mark territory on was Bra-Man. I love that damn character.

I RAN INTO AN OLD FLING OF YOURS

AND SHE HAD SOME INTERESTING THINGS TO SAY.

WHO AND WHAT?

SHE SAYS YOU USED TO BUY HER FLOWERS?

JENNY.

YEAH, I'M A SWEETHEART.

YOU BOUGHT A WOMAN FLOWERS?

WHY?

TO SHOW MY AFFECTION.

I NEVER GOT THE WHOLE "FLOWERS" THING.

THEY DIE SO QUICKLY.

AND SO DOES MY AFFECTION.

Is this not a valid point? Honestly now?

I'm sure at the time I had a valid reason why Rayne would be going home with Octopus lady, but looking back, I have no clue as to what that may have been.

Let's just assume there was magic.

SO YOU DECIDE IF YOU'RE COMING OVER TONIGHT?

UH, GIVE ME TEN MINUTES.

FIFTEEN SHOTS OF TEQUILA PLEASE,

IN ONE GIANT GLASS.

YOU'RE GOING TO HAVE TO DRINK A LOT MORE THAN THAT TO MAKE HER ATTRACTIVE.

YOU SEE THE TENTACLES TOO THOUGH, RIGHT?

On behalf of all white men, I would like to formally apologize for all our wrong doing throughout history. Our bad.

Now that that's behind us, perhaps everyone can chip in with their taxes?

I owe a word of thanks to the fine website of 'peopleofwalmart. com' for supplying me with so much inspiration for the ugly chicks in this book.

HALLOWEEN COME EARLY THIS YEAR?

SMART ASS. I TRIED TO APPLY FOR A TAX BREAK

AND HOW DID IT GO?

IT DIDN'T.

APPARENTLY BEING A NATIVE IS SOMETHING YOU HAVE TO BE BORN INTO.

SO YOU JUST GOING TO BUCK UP AND PAY YOUR FULL TAXES?

HELL NO.

I'VE STILL GOT PLAN B.

GET THE DOOR FOR ME, WILL YOU?

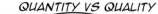

Panel 1:
HOW CAN YOU MANAGE TO STOOP SO LOW?

I PUT A LOT OF EFFORT INTO IT.

Panel 2:
WHAT'S GOING ON?

RAYNE'S TRYING TO GET A TAX BREAK BY CLAIMING TO BE RECENTLY CRIPPLED.

HOW TWISTED IS THAT?

Panel 4:
WHILE YOU'RE THERE, GET ME A HANDICAPPED STICKER FOR MY CAR.

GOTCHA.

No one in the cast of LICD will ever be as corrupt as Rayne, yet I couldn't make each character be a wet blanket. That's John's position and he holds on to it tightly.

Up until now, we've seen Baby a few times, but she hadn't yet been used in a punch line role. It was way past time to show the readers we had at the time that Baby was more than just background noise.

Baby's appearances in the strips, either scripted by Sohmer or randomly inserted by me, adds an element of the real world. She's a cat, and we are sharing her space.

KITTYKITTYKITTYKITTY

Panel 1:
I JUST DON'T KNOW WHAT I'M DOING.

WITH WOMEN THAT IS.

I MEAN, I'M GREAT WITH SLEEPING WITH THEM, BUT THAT'S ABOUT IT.

Panel 2:
IS THERE SOMETHING WRONG WITH ME?

WHAT IF I'M NEVER ABLE TO REALLY CONNECT WITH ANYONE?

Panel 3:
YEAH, YOU'RE RIGHT.

HONESTLY, YOU'RE THE ONLY ONE I CAN TALK TO ABOUT THIS SORT OF THING.

I'D BE LOST WITHOUT YOU.

Panel 4:
TREAT?

SHAKE SHAKE

DID YOU HEAR?

WATCHING MOVIE.

NO TALK.

MICK MET A GIRL, AND THEY REALLY HIT IT OFF

HE'S ON HIS WAY UP NOW TO INTRODUCE HER TO US,

MOO-VIE.

WE'VE MET...

GUYS, THIS IS SUZIE

DOWN IN FRONT.

WE...AH...

DATED FOR CLOSE TO A YEAR.

I'M JUST GOING TO PAUSE THIS.

We'd done a few arcs thus far, most of them rather quick. I was itching to see if I could tell a story in more than five days. Now watch as I make you, the comic reader, dance to my music like a puppet on strings.

DANCE, PUPPET! DANCE!

...okay, so maybe not out of the left field like I hoped, yet I was still fairly proud of this obvious further plot twist to Mick's new girlfriend.

ANYTHING ELSE I SHOULD KNOW?

HAVE YOU SLEPT WITH ANY OTHER OF MY FRIENDS?

WHAT ARE YOU STARING AT ME FOR?

UM... RAYNE...

I'VE NEVER TOUCHED THIS GIRL –

I USED TO HAVE BLONDE HAIR.

– MORE THAN ONCE.

SIX TIMES.

YOU'RE NOT HELPING.

WHERE'S MICK?

KITCHEN.

AND RAYNE?

WITH HIM.

WHY'D THEY LEAVE YOU HERE ALONE?

THEY STARTED FIGHTING ABOUT ME, BUT DECIDED TO TALK ABOUT THE SITUATION IN PRIVATE.

I'M A LITTLE WORRIED, JOHN.

THE LAST THING I WANT TO DO IS COME BETWEEN THOSE TWO.

I BETTER GO IN THERE AND MAKE SURE THEY'RE NOT KILLING EACH OTHER.

SO SHE GIVES GOOD—

OH YEAH.

Hugs. She gives good hugs.

Yeah. Like everyone is believing that.

AOHELL

I HAVE TO STAY HOME FOR 72 HOURS?

IF YOU WISH TO HAVE YOUR INTERNET SERVICE REPAIRED, THEN YES, MR. SUMMERS.

HOW CAN YOU EXPECT ME TO JUST SIT AT HOME FOR THREE STRAIGHT DAYS TO WAIT FOR A TECHNICIAN?

THERE'S NOTHING I CAN DO, MR. SUMMERS.

THIS IS UNBELIEVABLE.

WHAT DID I EVER TO YOU?

YOU TOLD MY PARENTS I HAD A FONDNESS FOR ANIMAL PORNOGRAPHY.

...LISA?

YEAH, WE'RE NEVER GETTING OUR INTERNET FIXED.

I KNEW WE SHOULDN'T HAVE PUT ANY OF THE UTILITIES UNDER YOUR NAME.

THEY TOOK AWAY MY DOG!

Back in those days of yore, I was writing a strip the day before it was published online. There was no such thing as a 'buffer' or 'writing ahead' or 'personal hygiene'. For the most part, I was able to stay on track with an idea in progress, but every now and then a gag would jump into my head that I had to put to paper immediately.

Patience wasn't really my thing.

Good thing that I've since matured.

Heh.

And back to the story at hand...

SO YOU GUYS ARE REALLY COOL WITH ME DATING SUZIE?

AS LONG AS YOU'RE HAPPY, MAN.

BUT, YOU'RE GOING TO HAVE TO LET RAYNE GET THE "WHORE" JOKES OUT OF HIS SYSTEM BEFORE HE EXPLODES.

I UNDERSTAND. GO AHEAD.

WHY DID SUZIE CROSS THE ROAD?

TO SLEEP WITH THAT SIDE OF THE STREET...

TO PAY HER PIMP...

BECAUSE THAT'S WHERE THE STD CLINIC WAS...

SHE HAD FINISHED WITH THE ODD NUMBERED HOUSES...

SHE HADN'T HAD SEX WITH THE CHICKEN YET...

SIT DOWN.

THIS IS GOING TO TAKE A WHILE.

YOU DON'T FIND IT IRONIC,

WHAT DO YOU MEAN?

YOU CALLING SOMEONE ELSE A WHORE?

HOW MANY WOMEN HAVE YOU SLEPT WITH?

HEY, THAT'S DIFFERENT.

I LOVED EACH AND EVERY ONE OF THEM.

VERY DEEPLY.

YOU REALLY EXPECT US TO BELIEVE THAT?

I'M REALLY AN EMOTIONAL GUY—

OH SHUT UP.

I was surprised at how large a role Suzie had in these early strips. I have the feeling she's still not done with Mick either.

The devout among you know that this is far from the last time we'll be seeing Suzie.

You also know that Jesus loves eggplant.

IT WAS A ROUGH FIRST COUPLE OF WEEKS FOR US,

BUT WE PULLED THROUGH.

SO YOU'RE REALLY OKAY WITH THE FACT THAT I'VE SLEPT WITH RAYNE AND JOHN?

YEAH, IT DOESN'T AFFECT HOW I SEE YOU OR MY FEELINGS FOR YOU.

PROMISE.

OKAY....

WHAT'S WRONG HONEY?

AND IT'S BACK TO THERAPY FOR ME.

I'M ALL OUT OF LOVE, I'M SO LOST WITHOUT YOU.

I KNOW YOU WERE RIGHT, BELIEVING FOR SO LONG

I 'M ALL OUT OF LOVE, WHAT AM I WITHOUT YOU

I CAN'T BE TOO LATE TO SAY THAT I WAS SO WRONG

DID YOU HONESTLY THINK THAT SINGING AIR SUPPLY SONGS WOULD MAKE ME FORGET YOU HAD SEX WITH MY SISTER?

NO, BUT I WAS HOPING IT'D AT LEAST MAKE UP FOR SLEEPING WITH YOUR COUSIN.

I want to live in a world where singing Air Supply to a woman can right any wrong.

Wow. That's so.... gay.

THERE'S A LETTER HERE FOR YOU.

IT'S AN INVITATION TO AN ENGAGEMENT PARTY.

YOU READ MY MAIL?

WANT TO KNOW WHO'S GETTING MARRIED?

I WANT TO KNOW WHY YOU'RE GOING THROUGH MY MAIL.

WHAT'S THE BIG DEAL?

YOU GO THROUGH MY STUFF ALL THE TIME!

I DO NOT.

SO MY SILK BRAS JUST MAGICALLY DISAPPEARED?

ALL SIX OF THEM?

SILK IS SOFT.

The relationship between Rayne and Issa was always key to the development of both their characters. Why does Issa put up with him, and why does Rayne not sleep with her?

I genuinely wish that I could shave that quickly.

Do I really need to point out that while you have less chin than Rayne you have significantly more scalp to shave. I think there's your problem.

By showing the reader that Rayne was once an actual sweetheart, or at least pretended to be in the last panel, we opened the door to later reveal what changed him. What would happen in the intervening years to turn a sweet 13 year old into the man-whore that is Rayne?

 I've been trying to solve for X for the last 31 years.

My father-in-law has mastered this amazing ability, as did his father before him. I think it's a masonic secret.

 Once everyone started using whip cream, it became less fun to introduce it into the love making process. But sour cream...no one's using sour cream!

No one is using spray cheese either. There's a reason for that.

A CASE OF THE CHIVES

THANK YOU, CYRANO

 If The Tao of Rayne had been around during these early days, this would have worked perfectly well for that feature.

While I enjoy Trevor's art, the one thing I was never satisfied with was his rendition of Issa. She always came off a little too Olive Oyl to carry the gags that relied on her powerful sexuality.

DIVIDED HE FALLS

When you go on to the next strip, you'll notice it has nothing to do with this wedding. The reason is because I began to completely loathe what I was writing partway through. Rather than keep doing something I hated, I took the cowards way out and pretended it never happened.

This was the first and last time I'd ever done that.

I'll say it again: I'm a wonderful parent.

Over the years, we've introduced many features to the comic, including The Tao of Rayne, Rayne's Guide to... and others. The poem, however, the poem will always be my favorite.

WHO'S SCRUFFY LOOKING?!

A POEM

IT STARTED SO WELL, THAT LATE WINTER'S NIGHT

QUITE HOT SHE LOOKED, I MUST SAY, AT FIRST SIGHT

HER SHIRT SHE TOOK OFF, WITH NAUGHT EVEN A CARE

AND THAT'S WHEN I SAW, THIS GIRL WAS COVERED IN HAIR

AND SO I SAID ON TO HER, WHILE I DO CRAVE SOME NOOKIE

I'LL BE DAMNED MY DEAR, IF I SLEEP WITH A WOOKIE

SNAP

I love Rayne's poetry corner. One of the things I most enjoy is trying not to repeat myself in terms of presentation and venue. It's great fun.

PLUS ÇA CHANGE

RAYNE? IS THAT YOU?

DEPENDS ON WHO'S ASKING.

CAN'T BELIEVE YOU DON'T RECOGNIZE YOUR OLD BABYSITTER.

KAREN!?!

THE LAST TIME I SAW YOU, YOU WERE SLEEPING NAKED ON THE FLOOR, IN A PUDDLE OF YOUR OWN DROOL.

WASN'T THAT YESTER—

OH SHUT UP.

For the record, Rayne does not drink coffee. There's hot chocolate in that cup.

I'm not sure if this scenario falls under the list of every man's dream, yet I'm sure it at least ranks in the top ten.

Which could help explain the ugly tentacles chick.

MOVING FURNITURE OR THE EARTH?

I WAS THINKING, MAYBE YOU COULD HELP ME WITH SOMETHING.

ANYTHING.

I JUST MOVED INTO A NEW PLACE LAST WEEK,

BUT I COULD REALLY USE SOME MUSCLE IN SETTING THE FURNITURE.

MORE THAN HAPPY TO.

GREAT, RAYNE!

I'LL CALL YOU IN THE NEXT FEW DAYS, AND WE'LL MAKE A WHOLE NIGHT OUT OF IT.

IT'S TIMES LIKE THESE I WISH I BELIEVED IN GOD SO I'D HAVE SOMEONE TO THANK.

SO SAY WE ALL

WHAT'S SO FUNNY?

JUST SAW A KID FALL OFF HIS BIKE.

HARD.

SERIOUSLY, HE MUST HAVE FLEW LIKE TEN FEET.

DID YOU CHECK TO SEE IF THE KID WAS ALRIGHT?

I'M A HORRIBLE PERSON.

Yeah....maybe this whole procreation thing wasn't my best call.

Just one word. eBay.

RAYNE, KAREN'S ON THE PHONE!

SHE SAYS TO HURRY UP, SHE'S IN A RUSH.

TIME FOR RAYNE PSYCHOLOGY 101.

HIS FIRST REACTION IS:

"I'M RAYNE SUMMERS.

I DON'T RUN FOR THE PHONE WHEN A WOMAN CALLS,

THEY RUN WHEN I CALL!"

THIS THOUGHT WILL QUICKLY BE FOLLOWED WITH:

"THEN AGAIN, SHE'S SO DAMN HOT.

PLUS, I'VE NEVER BEEN WITH AN OLDER WOMAN BEFORE.

AND SHE'S SO HOT.

HOT. HOT. HOT.

WHAT IF SHE HANGS UP?"

CLASS DISMISSED.

John doesn't get smug very often, but when he does, he's dead on.

I remember very clearly the discussion in the forum regarding this particular strip. Apparently, it wasn't clear what Rayne was doing in that last panel. Should it still remain a mystery to you, I'll tell you.

He's very happy.

DON'T GET YOUR HOPES UP.

JUST BECAUSE KAREN INVITED YOU OVER DOESN'T MEAN ANYTHING IS GOING TO HAPPEN.

SHE WAS YOUR BABYSITTER, SHE WON'T—

AREN'T YOU GOING TO COME IN?

JUST GIVE ME ONE SECOND.

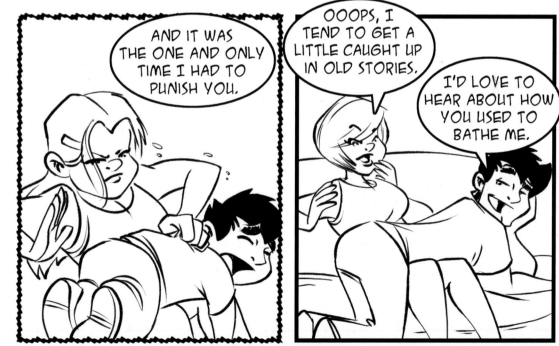

Rayne is so street, man. Totally.

LOOK, IF YOU HAD ONE SHOT, ONE OPPORTUNITY...

TO SEIZE EVERYTHING YOU EVER WANTED.

ONE MOMENT.

WOULD YOU CAPTURE IT OR JUST LET IT SLIP?

I NEVER WOULD HAVE EXPECTED SOMEONE SO YOUNG

TO BE SO DEEP.

OH, THERE GOES GRAVITY.

SO, LOOKING FORWARD TO MIDDLE AGE?

DO PEOPLE TELL YOU THAT YOU'RE A LITTLE STUPID?

QUITE OFTEN.

While the joke here is amusing, I admit that it was out of character for Rayne. He doesn't blow these moments. His friends do.

WHAT'S WRONG?

JUST THINKING THAT MAYBE THIS ISN'T THE BEST IDEA.

WHY NOT?

FIRST OFF, YOU'RE ABOUT FIFTEEN YEARS OLDER THAN I AM

AND SECONDLY, YOU USED TO BABY-SIT FOR ME.

YOU'RE MISSING THE OBVIOUS PLUS SIDE TO THIS.

WHICH IS?

I'M 39, YOU'RE 24.

I HAVE NO INTEREST IN ANY FUTURE WITH YOU EXCEPT FOR A FEW HOURS OF RAVAGING SEX.

SOLD!

Again, why is he attempting to ruin this for himself?

Writing like this makes me want to put my head through a window. That'll teach it.

If I could go back and re-write this strip a little, all I'd do is have Rayne chuckle throughout the whole thing. He'd be amused at the situation, not out of sorts.

In hindsight I think your comedic instinct on this was correct. Rayne is out-maneuvered at his own game. If he wasn't, this would have been a pretty straight forward encounter.

HELLO POT? THIS IS KETTLE..

THAT.

RIGHT THERE.

THAT WAS INCREDIBLE.

IT WAS ALRIGHT.

ALRIGHT?!? WHAT—

LISTEN RAYNE,

I NEED TO GET UP EARLY TOMORROW MORNING

SO YOU SHOULD PROBABLY HEAD HOME.

WE'LL TALK AGAIN REAL SOON.

I'LL CALL.

PROMISE.

WAIT A—

THE IRONY OF THIS SITUATION IS NOT LOST ON ME.

RAYNE'S GUIDE TO: THE OPPOSITE SEX

WOMEN LOVE AN HONEST MAN

HOW DO I LOOK?

JUST GREAT,

THOUGH YOU LOOKED EVEN BETTER WITH THE BLUE TOP.

HOW DO I LOOK?

WILLY CALLED,

HE'S TRYING TO FREE YOU.

BUT SOMETIMES THEY DON'T.

If you didn't laugh at this one, it's not my fault. There's obviously something significantly wrong with you.

One of my biggest pet peeves about comic strips is when every character has the exact same speech pattern, when any line could be said by any given character and it wouldn't sound out of place. Aware of this, I made a concerted effort to avoid it. Hopefully it's noticeable.

HONESTLY SUZIE,

HOW MANY GUYS HAVE YOU BEEN WITH?

A FEW.

JUST GIVE ME A NUMBER.

NOT MORE THAN THIRTY GUYS.

THIRTY GUYS?

YOU'VE SLEPT WITH THIRTY GUYS?

MIGHT BE A LITTLE MORE THAN THAT.

AND WE'RE OFF TO THE CLINIC.

The same criteria works visually as well. Many novice cartoonists don't realize that simply changing hair colour isn't enough to make a character stand out as an individual.

I completely forgot about this arc...hope it's funny.

S'okay. I got yer back on it.

WHY ARE YOU SO UNCOMFORTABLE HERE?

IT'S NOT THE PLACE, IT'S THE PEOPLE.

IT'S JUST A CLINIC.

I DON'T WANT TO CATCH ANYTHING.

NO I'M NOT.

YOU'RE PARANOID AND IGNORANT.

TAKE THIS GIRL NEXT TO ME FOR EXAMPLE.

SHE LOOKS NORMAL,

BUT I HAVE NO IDEA WHAT LOVELY STD SHE'S CARRYING.

FOR ALL I KNOW, SHE COULD BE ON HER EIGHTH CASE OF GONORRHEA.

BEEN WAITING LONG?

MICK? WHAT ARE YOU—

QUIET DOWN.

DON'T CALL ME THAT.

WHY'S THAT?

HE GAVE HIS NAME AS 'PEDRO' WHEN HE CHECKED IN.

DUDE, THERE'S NOTHING TO BE EMBARRASSED ABOUT.

THIS IS PERFECTLY NORMAL. EVERYONE GOES THROUGH THIS AT ONE POINT OR ANOTHER.

RAYNE, YOUR USUAL ROOM IS READY.

SOME MORE THAN OTHERS.

In retrospect, I believe I was trying to show that while Rayne is promiscuous, he's also obsessive about his sexual health.

Panel 1: I'M SORRY TO SAY, BUT I'M AFRAID YOU HAVE A SMALL CASE OF GENITAL WARTS.

Panel 2: IS IT ALRIGHT IF I START CRYING, OR WOULD YOU PREFER I TAKE IT OUTSIDE?

RELAX, MICK. IT'S FAIRLY EASY TO CURE.

ONE NEEDLE THROUGH THE TIP OF YOUR PENIS, AND WE'RE DONE.

Panel 4: I SOMETIMES FEEL THAT PEOPLE WERE PUT ON THIS PLANET JUST TO AMUSE ME.

 If you didn't just cringe, you don't have junk.

One thing I have learned as a caricaturist is that medical professionals love physical humour in their cartoons.

Panel 1: LEAST I COULD DO MAILBOX

AN ANONYMOUS READER WRITES:

'STD'S ARE NOT REAL.

THEY ARE TOOLS OF THE CATHOLIC CHURCH MADE TO SCARE KIDS INTO THINKING SEX IS DANGEROUS!'

Panel 2: YOU HEARD THAT?

Panel 3: STD'S NOT REAL?

ARE YOU #N!@% KIDDING ME?

Panel 4: I'VE GOT THE SYPHILIS SCARS TO PROVE IT YOU SON OF—

 It amazes me the things that I've forgotten while doing Least I Could Do. If you had asked me a few days ago about LICD Mailbox, I would have stared blankly at you until you got uncomfortable enough to leave.

It was a fun feature, though.

YAWN

WOULD YOU STOP POSTING YOUR TEST RESULTS ON THE FRIDGE?

I THOUGHT YOU'D BE PROUD OF ME.

Rayne wasn't much of a student as a child so it's not surprising he'd seek approval for other accomplishments.

Wow. That wasn't funny, well plotted or in character. Swing and a miss!

DOG TOYS

WANT TO GO TALK TO THOSE TWO OVER THERE?

SURE, AS LONG AS I GET THE FATTIE.

HELL NO, SHE'S MINE.

YOU TAKE THE OTHER ONE.

IF YOU INSIST.

I DO. I REALLY DO.

REVERSE PSYCHOLOGY BE DAMNED.

Thank goodness it's at least exceptionally well drawn! Right?

Right?!

SO FIRST YOU STARTED WITH ANGELA,

WHOSE WEIGHT PROBLEMS WERE ONLY OVERSHADOWED BY HER ODOR.

THEN YOU MOVED ON TO ALYSSA.

SHE HAD A WICKED BODY, BUT THE FACIAL HAIR THING DIDN'T DO IT FOR ME.

FINALLY, YOU MADE A PLAY FOR CARA.

THOUGH SHE WAS BY FAR THE BEST OF THE LOT,

THE CONSTANT SPITTING REALLY WAS NOT APPEALING.

AND ALL THREE OF **THEM** SHOT YOU DOWN?

OH LOOK.

THERE GOES MY SELF ESTEEM.

Quick recovery by the writer!

(me)

HI THERE,

I WAS HOPING YOU COULD HELP ME.

MY NAME IS JENNIFER.

MY FRIEND JOHN OVER THERE IS HAVING A ROUGH NIGHT,

AND I'D REALLY LIKE TO FIND HIM AN ATTRACTIVE WOMAN SUCH AS YOURSELF.

DO YOU THINK YOU MIGHT BE INTERESTED?

MY NAME IS JENNIFER,

I LIKE TO DANCE.

YOU'LL DO NICELY.

There are times I wish I could see the world through Lar's eyes, where every women on the planet wears a halter top.

Not every woman! Just the generic sluts and bimbos.

I FEEL KIND OF BAD.

WHAT'S WRONG NOW?

JENNIFER'S WILLING TO COME HOME WITH ME,

BUT IT DOESN'T SEEM FAIR TO HER.

IT'S LIKE TAKING ADVANTAGE OF THE MENTALLY HANDICAPPED.

YOU'RE THINKING ABOUT IT RIGHT NOW, AREN'T YOU?

IT'S LIKE TELLING SOMEONE *NOT* TO THINK OF A PINK HORSE.

Oh look, the third panel has no dialogue. Where have I done that before?

EVERY DAMN STRIP. Le sigh.

But the pictures sell it! Right?!

VALIDATE MEEEEE!

I wish I was in the room when they decided that what the internet really needed was pictures and video of women having intercourse with goats.

I would have agreed.

WHAT'S WITH THE SIGN?

BECAUSE OF LAST WEEK'S STORYLINE,

OUR 'CREATORS' WANTED TO PROVIDE A LINK FOR MORE INFORMATION ON STDS.

WWW.I-STD.COM

SERIOUSLY?

WE'RE A PUBLIC SERVICE ANNOUNCEMENT STRIP NOW?

WWW.I-STD.COM

WHAT ARE YOU DOING?

WWW.I-STD.COM

JUST MY PART TO HELP THE COMMUNITY.

WWW.FARMSEX.COM

YEAH!

A POEM

YEAH!

YOU SPOKE TO YOUR FRIENDS, AND THEIR WORDS WERE NOT KIND

THEY SAID THAT TO DATE ME, YOU'D BE OUT OF YOUR MIND

SO THEY WARN AND COMPLAIN, AND THEY YELL STAY AWAY

FOR THAT MR. RAYNE SUMMERS, WILL TAKE NO TIME TO STRAY

BUT THERE'S A SECRET THEY'RE NOT TELLING,

IN THE MIDST OF THEIR MOB LYNCHES

THE RUMORS ARE TRUE, I WEIGH IN AT EIGHTEEN INCHES

ET TU, MICK?

IT'S JUST PAINT.

AVENGE MY DEATH.

WHEN SHADOW DESCENDS ON THE FOREST, THE TRUE HUNTER APPEARS.

KNOWING HIS SUPERIOR SKILLS IN STEALTH WILL ALLOW HIM TO GET THE DROP ON THE UNSUSPECTING ENEMY, THE HUNTER SURVEYS THE LAND LIKE A HAWK.

THE HUNTER IS PATIENT, KNOWING NO FEAR. HE IS SEEKING THE ELUSIVE TARGET, READY TO BESTOW A HORRIBLE WRATH UPON HIM.

APPROPRIATE RESPONSES...

CAN'T GET DOWN FROM THE TREE, CAN YOU?

CLIK

THE TARGET HAS BEEN LOCATED.

Obviously this was written shortly after I played paintball. Though Paintball and I have a storied history, sometimes involving my hospitalization, I keep playing. When will I learn?

Probably never...

I may have just answered my own rhetorical question.

Weird.

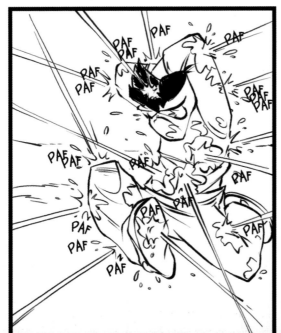

 After a couple thousand strips, the 100 milestone doesn't seem that exciting anymore.

BYE BABY.

I LOVE YOU.

I LOVE YOU MORE.

AND JULIE MAKES ONE HUNDRED!

I'M A WHORE.

LEAST I COULD DO MAILBOX

AN ANONYMOUS READER WRITES:

"WHERE DOES RAYNE GET ALL OF HIS MONEY?"

I'VE OFTEN WONDERED THAT MYSELF.

SMART ASS.

I'M A COLUMNIST FOR THE LOCAL PAPER HERE IN THE CITY.

USUALLY, THE DAILY COLUMN FOCUSES ON POP CULTURE AND ENTERTAINMENT,

BUT ONCE IN A WHILE I'LL TACKLE AN IMPORTANT ISSUE.

I THINK WHAT HE'S REALLY ASKING

IS WHETHER YOU'VE EVER CHARGED WOMEN FOR SEX?

NO COMMENT.

H-uh. I really did like this feature, didn't I?

Why do I keep asking you questions that you can't answer?

...Dammit.

There once was a time when we didn't have an active online forum for these questions to be answered. That's probably why the LICD mailbox has faded away.

Panel 1: AND FOR YOU MA'AM? / I'LL HAVE THE SMOTHERED CHICKEN WITH A SIDE OF—

Panel 2: WHAT'S SO FUNNY? / SMOTHERED CHICKEN...

Panel 4: IF YOU WANTED TO ASK HIM TO LEAVE, I'D UNDERSTAND. / HA HA HA HA HA HA HA

POINT, COUNTERPOINT

Panel 5: I WAS TALKING ABOUT YOU THE OTHER DAY. / MMMM?

Panel 6: WITH TAMARA. / SHE WAS WONDERING HOW YOU AND I HAVE BEEN FRIENDS FOR SO LONG.

Panel 7: I THINK WHAT SHE WAS REALLY GETTING AT / WAS HOW I WAS HAVING A HEALTHY FRIENDSHIP WITH AN OBVIOUS WOMANIZER LIKE YOU.

Panel 8: YESTERDAY, I SPENT SIX HOURS ON THE INTERNET LOOKING FOR AN AMATEUR PORN STAR WHO LOOKED LIKE YOU. / VERY HEALTHY.

Erica Campbell.

HOW WAS EVERYTHING?
WONDERFUL.
JUST GREAT.

IS ONE BILL ALL RIGHT,
OR SHOULD I SEPARATE IT?
SEPA-

SHE'S GOOD.
I KNOW.

Why don't I have breasts?

I think this might be the hottest I've ever drawn Issa to date.

You're welcome.

RAYNE, I'M PREGNANT.
MelloYello asks: How would you stay smooth?

DON'T WORRY SWEETHEART,
WE'LL GET THROUGH THIS TOGETHER.
DING! a.

A FATHER?
I'M GOING TO BE A FATHER?
DING! b.

GIVE ME AN A!
GIVE ME A B!
GIVE ME AN O!
GIVE ME AN R!
DING! DING! DING! DING! DING! c. DING!

An abortion joke this early in a career would usually do bad things for a writer. Luckily for me, we had about six readers at the time and my e-mail wasn't working.

WHERE IS HE?

WHAT HAPPENED TO HIM?

JEBAS NO!

WHAT IF HE DOESN'T MAKE IT!?

DO SOMETHING!

HOMEWARD BOUND?

YEP.

RUN SHADOW, RUN!

There is one movie in this world that has the ability to make me cry every single time I watch...

I love you Shadow. I wish you were my dog.

LEAST I COULD DO MAILBOX

KAE WRITES IN:

"IS ISSA THE KIND OF FRIEND RAYNE CAN GET BENEFITS FROM?"

UNBELIEVABLE.

IS THIS REALLY WHAT YOU PEOPLE THINK OF ME?

THAT I WOULD STOOP SO LOW AS TO SLEEP WITH MY BEST FEMALE FRIEND?

JUST BECAUSE SHE'S SUPER HOT AND HAS THE MOST MAGICAL BREASTS I'VE EVER SEEN DOESN'T ..WOULDN'T...

NEVER...

WHERE WAS I GOING WITH THIS?

YOU WERE ABOUT TO ADMIT THAT YOU CONSTANTLY TRY TO SLEEP WITH ISSA, BUT FAIL MISERABLY.

THAT SOUNDS ABOUT RIGHT.

I'm not 100% certain, but I'm almost 8% sure that there's a passage in the bible regarding this.

And this is why you will never be pope.

They need to know this kind of thing already.

SO IT WASN'T A TOTAL LOSS

FOR JEBAS' SAKE.

AFTER THREE HOURS IN THE BAD BOY CHAIR YOU'RE RIGHT BACK HERE?

YOU EVEN BROUGHT A FRIEND.

ENOUGH.

BOTH OF YOU NEED HELP.

I'M GOING TO CANCEL YOUR MEMBERSHIP OF...

LARGEBREASTEDANOREXICS.COM?

AND THE MASSIVE MAGICAL BREASTS?

WITH THE ITTY BITTY BODIES?

Before you take the time to check, yes, someone does own this domain.

Credit where it's due. Jesus Christ made a pretty formidable entrance when he was introduced. But this?

I think this tops that.

*cough*pope would already know*cough*

FOR EVERYTHING ELSE, THERE'S HERPES

I CAN'T BELIEVE WE JUST SPENT AN ENTIRE DAY BUYING INTERNET PORN.

YEAH, I'M FEELING FAIRLY DIRTY.

WITH ALL THE FREE PORN OUT THERE,

WHAT WE JUST DID EQUATES TO PAYING FOR SEX.

WHICH YOU OF COURSE HAVE NEVER DONE.

NOPE.

YOU'VE NEVER BEEN WITH A PROSTITUTE?

NEVER.

WAS TEMPTED ONCE THOUGH...

SUCK FOR A BUCK

IT JUST SEEMS WRONG THAT I SPEND MORE ON A PACK OF GUM.

SUCK FOR A BUCK

It should be noted that the Suck for a Buck lady is based on a woman I met when I was driving downtown at the ripe ol' age of sixteen.

YOU SHOULD SEE THE FLOATS!

WHAT ARE YOU GUYS TALKING ABOUT?

THE JOYS OF DOUBLE STANDARDS.

MY PROBLEM IS, IF A GIRL SLEEPS WITH MORE THAN SEVEN GUYS, SHE'S CONSIDERED A SLUT.

BUT, SHOULD A GUY SCORE MORE THAN FIFTY WOMEN,

HE GETS A PARADE.

AND A TROPHY!

HE MADE THAT HIMSELF

50

WHEN WE MET, THERE WAS SOMETHING ABOUT YOU THAT JUST DREW ME IN.

AND NOW I FIND THAT IT'S ALL A LIE.

WHAT I THOUGHT WAS THERE WAS NOTHING MORE THAN AN ILLUSION.

THIS HURTS.

NOW PLEASE, TAKE YOUR PUSHUP BRA AND GO.

In theory, I understand the concept of the pushup Bra. In practicality however, all it ends up doing is hurting people.

People like men.

ONE HUNDRED AND FIFTEEN.

ONE HUNDRED AND FIFTEEN STRIPS, OVER FOUR MONTHS,

AND I HAVEN'T SAID MORE THAN THREE WORDS.

I'M A REGULAR CHARACTER IN THIS STRIP!

LOGIC DICTATES I SHOW UP MORE THAN ONCE A YEAR.

I'M AN IMPORTANT PART OF THIS CAST AND THE OTHERS DEFINITELY NEED ME.

WHAT'S GOING ON?

I THINK WE'RE BEING ROBBED.

Who is this guy?

ANTI MAN

I still wonder whatever happened to Rob. Though, considering I'm the writer, maybe this is something I should know.

There's some strange cosmc harmony that there's as many words for penis as there are for a man who has been emasculated by his lady.

MORE WHIPPED THAN A SINGAPORE GRAFFITI ARTIST

Okay, how about this:

Rob is actually an alien and was returned to the mothership. The alien reunion was something special.

You should've been there.

ROB! TWO MORE MINUTES!

BETH NEEDS ME TO TAKE HER SHOPPING.

WHAT?

JUST LOOKING TO SEE IF THE LEASH LEAVES ANY MARKS.

FORGIVE ME FATHER, FOR I HAVE SINNED.

YOU KNOW ME, I'M NOT EXACTLY MR. MORALITY.

BUT EVEN I HAVE MY LIMITS,

AND I FEAR THAT I MAY HAVE CROSSED THEM.

I DID SOMETHING HORRIBLE, FATHER.

I'M JUST NOT SURE HOW TO DEAL WITH THE CONSEQUENCES.

MY SON,

I'VE HEARD MOST OF YOUR TALES OF TEQUILA AND LESBIANS.

LAST TUESDAY

TONIGHT, ON BIG BROTHER...

Jebas, I did a Big Brother strip? Was there any level to which I would not stoop?

TURN AROUND.

HANDS ON THE VEHICLE.

PARDON?

YOU MIND IF I TURN ON THE RADIO, OFFICER?

YOU KNOW, TO SET THE MOOD.

THERE'S NO WAY WE'RE GETTING THROUGH THIS WITHOUT ME SHOOTING YOU AT LEAST ONCE.

BE AS ROUGH AS YOU NEED TO BE.

It's a fairly honest mistake, I think. You would think the officer would be a little more understanding. Shouldn't they be covering this sort of scenario at the Police Academy?

Doo doo doo....

(That's the Police Academy Theme song if you were wondering)

SO MUCH FOR MIRANDA RIGHTS

PAT PAT PAT

PAT PAT PAT PAT

THE REASON I PULLED YOU OVER—

LESS TALK.

MORE FOREPLAY.

At last, we come to the final Trevor-era strip and the end of our little voyage together down memory lane.

POOR LI'L ROADRUNNER

I MIGHT HAVE DESERVED THIS.

GRRRRRR

 Though these hundred-odd strips are hardly a drop in the bucket when compared to what we've done since, I'm forced to admit that there's still something special about them. They are, and will always be, the Beginning of Least I Could Do.

No matter how embarrassed I may be of some of them...

Sohmer and I understand that there are the purist among you who have been hankering to see the online collection finally brought together like this and will likely still feel a bit disappointed that the work of Trevor cannot properly be readied for print. Never fear! In an effort to please even those out there who would like a hardcopy of the work, regardless of the quality, here are the original strips, converted from web resolution to a printable format. Enjoy!

LEAST I COULD DO — by Ryan Sohmer and Trevor Adams

DID YOU HEAR? / WATCHING MOVIE. NO TALK. / MICK MET A GIRL, AND THEY REALLY HIT IT OFF. HE'S ON HIS WAY UP NOW TO INTRODUCE HER TO US. / MOO-VIE. / GUYS, THIS IS SUZIE / WE'VE MET... / DOWN IN FRONT. / WE...AH...DATED FOR CLOSE TO A YEAR. / I'M JUST GOING TO PAUSE THIS.

ANYTHING ELSE I SHOULD KNOW? HAVE YOU SLEPT WITH ANY OTHER OF MY FRIENDS? / WHAT ARE YOU STARING AT ME FOR? I'VE NEVER TOUCHED THIS GIRL. / UM, RAYNE. I USED TO HAVE BLONDE HAIR. / -MORE THAN ONCE. / SIX TIMES. / YOU'RE NOT HELPING.

LEAST I COULD DO — by Ryan Sohmer and Trevor Adams

WHERE'S MICK? / KITCHEN. / AND RAYNE? / WITH HIM. / WHY'D THEY LEAVE YOU HERE ALONE? / THEY STARTED FIGHTING ABOUT ME, BUT DECIDED TO TALK ABOUT THE SITUATION IN PRIVATE. / I'M A LITTLE WORRIED, JOHN. THE LAST THING I WANT TO DO IS COME BETWEEN THOSE TWO. / I BETTER GO IN THERE AND MAKE SURE THEY'RE NOT KILLING EACH OTHER. / OH YEAH. / SO SHE GIVES GOOD-

I HAVE TO STAY HOME FOR 72 HOURS? / IF YOU WISH TO HAVE YOUR INTERNET SERVICE REPAIRED, THEN YES, MR. SUMMERS. / HOW CAN YOU EXPECT ME TO JUST SIT AT HOME FOR THREE STRAIGHT DAYS TO WAIT FOR A TECHNICIAN? / THERE'S NOTHING I CAN DO, MR. SUMMERS. / THIS IS UNBELIEVABLE. WHAT DID I EVER DO TO YOU? / YOU TOLD MY PARENTS I HAD A FONDNESS FOR ANIMAL PORNOGRAPHY. / LISA? / YES, RAYNE. / YEAH, WE'RE NEVER GETTING OUR INTERNET FIXED. / I KNEW WE SHOULDN'T HAVE PUT ANY OF THE UTILITIES UNDER YOUR NAME. / THEY TOOK AWAY MY DOG!

LEAST I COULD DO — by Ryan Sohmer and Trevor Adams

SO YOU GUYS ARE REALLY COOL WITH ME DATING SUZIE? / AS LONG AS YOU'RE HAPPY, MAN. / BUT YOU'RE GOING TO HAVE TO LET RAYNE GET THE "WHORE" JOKES OUT OF HIS SYSTEM BEFORE HE EXPLODES. / I UNDERSTAND. GO AHEAD. / WHY DID SUZIE CROSS THE ROAD? / TO SLEEP WITH THAT SIDE OF THE STREET. / TO PAY HER PIMP. / BECAUSE THAT'S WHERE THE STD CLINIC WAS. / SHE HAD FINISHED WITH THE ODD NUMBERED HOUSES. / SHE HADN'T HAD SEX WITH THE CHICKEN YET. / SIT DOWN. THIS IS GOING TO TAKE A WHILE.

YOU DON'T FIND IT IRONIC, YOU CALLING SOMEONE ELSE A WHORE? / WHAT DO YOU MEAN? / HOW MANY WOMEN HAVE YOU SLEPT WITH? / HEY, THAT'S DIFFERENT. I LOVED EACH AND EVERY ONE OF THEM. VERY DEEPLY. / YOU REALLY EXPECT US TO BELIEVE THAT? / I'M REALLY AN EMOTIONAL GUY- / OH SHUT UP

LEAST I COULD DO — by Ryan Sohmer and Trevor Adams

IT WAS A ROUGH FIRST COUPLE OF WEEKS FOR US, BUT WE PULLED THROUGH. / SO YOU'RE REALLY OKAY WITH THE FACT THAT I'VE SLEPT WITH RAYNE AND JOHN. / YEAH, IT WON'T AFFECT HOW I SEE YOU. BESIDES WHICH, I'M JUST NOT GOING TO THINK ABOUT- / WHAT THE...! / WHAT'S WRONG HONEY? / AND IT'S BACK TO THERAPY FOR ME.

I'M ALL OUT OF LOVE, I'M SO LOST WITHOUT YOU / I KNOW YOU WERE RIGHT, BELIEVING FOR SO LONG. / I'M ALL OUT OF LOVE, WHAT AM I WITHOUT YOU / I CAN'T BE TOO LATE, TO SAY THAT I WAS SO WRONG. / DID YOU HONESTLY THINK THAT SINGING AIR SUPPLY SONGS WOULD MAKE ME FORGET YOU HAD SEX WITH MY SISTER? / NO, BUT I WAS HOPING IT'D AT LEAST MAKE UP FOR SLEEPING WITH YOUR COUSIN.

LEAST I COULD DO — by Ryan Sohmer and Trevor Adams

THERE'S A LETTER HERE FOR YOU. IT'S AN INVITATION TO AN ENGAGEMENT PARTY. / YOU READ MY MAIL? / WANT TO KNOW WHO'S GETTING MARRIED? / I WANT TO KNOW WHY YOU'RE GOING THROUGH MY MAIL. / WHAT'S THE BIG DEAL? YOU GO THROUGH MY STUFF ALL THE TIME! / I DO NOT. / SO MY SILK BRAS JUST MAGICALLY DISAPPEARED? ALL SIX OF THEM? / SILK IS SOFT.

Copyright 2005, Ryan Sohmer and Trevor Adams. All rights reserved.

Holy-

Where did this strip come from?

WHAT HAVE YOU GOT PLANNED FOR TONIGHT?

COLUMN IS DUE TOMORROW.

GOT TO FINISH IT TONIGHT OR JUDY WILL KILL ME.

YOU?

CREATING LESSON PLANS,

GRADING SCIENCE PROJECTS,

MAKING A MATH POSTER

AND THE ALWAYS FUN "CALLING OF THE PARENTS".

TAK

BAR!

I ALREADY HAVE MY COAT ON!

BAM!

Alright, folks, I'll let you in on a little secret. Before Lar, Before Chad, Before Trevor, there was Marcus.

And maybe, just maybe, one day I'll tell you about it.

But not today.

I need a snack.

least i could do by ryan sohmer and markus ortiz

What have you got planned for tonight?

Column is due tomorrow, got to finish it tonight or Judy will kill me. You?

Creating lesson plans, grading science projects, making a math poster and the always fun "calling of the parents.

BAR!

I already have my coat on!

-Because I Can.